# Discovering Poetry 1

# Discovering poetry

*selected by E W Parker*
*revised by Michael Marland*

Book 1
Book 2
Book 3
Book 4  (Fresh fields)

*Companion series*

# Enjoying poetry

*selected by E W Parker*

2  For delight
3  For your pleasure
4  A galaxy of poems old and new

# Discovering poetry 1

chosen by E W Parker
the collection revised by Michael Marland

Longman

LONGMAN GROUP LIMITED
*Longman House,*
*Burnt Mill, Harlow, Essex and*
*Associated companies branches and representatives throughout the world*

*This selection © Longman Group Limited 1971*

*First published* 1953
*Seventh impression* 1965
*Second edition* 1971
*Sixth impression* 1982
*ISBN* 0 582 21899 3

*Printed in Singapore by*
*The Print House Pte Ltd*

# The poems

## Brothers and sisters

## Young lives

## Adventure

## Christmas

# The poets

# Acknowledgements

We are grateful to the following for permission to reproduce
copyright material:
Mrs George Bambridge and Macmillan & Co. for 'A smuggler's
Song' and 'Puck's Song' from *Puck of Pook's Hill* by Rudyard
Kipling; Barrie and Jenkins Ltd. for 'Neighbours' by Frances
Cornford from *Collected Poems*; Basil Blackwell for 'Micky
Thumps' from *Poetry for You* edited by Cecil Day Lewis; author
for 'To See the Rabbit' from *The Railings* by Alan Brownjohn;
Jonathan Cape Ltd. and Mrs H M Davis for 'Sheep' and 'The
Fog' from *The Complete Poems of W H Davies*; The Clarendon
Press for 'Robin Hood and the Bishop' from *The Oxford Book of
Ballads*; J M Dent & Sons Ltd. for the extract 'Man and
Beast' from *The Axe in the Wood* by Clifford Dyment; Gerald
Duckworth & Co. Ltd. for 'Matilda' by Hillaire Belloc from
*Cautionary Tales*; Eyre & Spottiswoode Ltd. for Psalms 100 and
121 from the text of the Authorised version of the Bible which
is Crown Copyright in England; Faber & Faber Ltd. for
'O What is that Sound' by W H Auden from *Collected Shorter
Poems 1927–1957*; 'Growltiger's Last Stand' by T S Eliot from
*Old Possum's Book of Practical Cats*; 'My Sister Jane' by Ted
Hughes from *Meet My Folks* and 'The Boy in the Barn' by
Herbert Read from *Collected Poems;* the author and author's
agent for 'Brother' and 'The Two Witches' by Robert Graves
from *Collected Poems*; Rupert Hart Davis Ltd. and author's
agents for 'The Ballad of the Bread Man' and 'Innocent's Song'
by Charles Causley; William Heinemann Ltd. for 'The Little
Brother' from *Collected Poems* by James Reeves; Author for
'The Eve of Christmas' by James Kirkup; Macmillan & Co. Ltd
for 'The Place's Fault' by Philip Hobsbaum; Macmillan & Co.
Ltd., The Macmillan Company of Canada Ltd. and The

# Man and beast

Hugging the ground by the lilac tree,
With shadows in conspiracy,

The black cat from the house next door
Waits with death in each bared claw

For the tender unwary bird
That all the summer I have heard

In the orchard singing. I hate
The cat that is its savage fate,

And choose a stone with which to send
Slayer not victim, to its end.

I look to where the black cat lies,
But drop my stone, seeing its eyes –

Who is it sins now, those eyes say,
You the hunter, or I the prey?

*Clifford Dyment*

# Five eyes

In Hans' old mill his three black cats
Watch his bins for the thieving rats.
Whisker and claw, they crouch in the night
Their five eyes smouldering green and bright;
Squeaks from the flour sacks, squeaks from where
The cold wind stirs on the empty stair,
Squeaking and scampering, everywhere.
Then down they pounce, now in, now out,
At whisking tail, and sniffing snout;
While lean old Hans he snores away
Till peep of light at break of day;
Then up he climbs to his creaking mill,
Out come his cats all grey with meal –
Jekkel, and Jessup, and one-eyed Jill.

*Walter de la Mare*

# Poem

As the cat
climbed over
the top of

the jamcloset
first the right
forefoot

carefully
then the hind
stepped down

into the pit of
the empty
flowerpot.

*William Carlos Williams*

# Growltiger's last stand

Growltiger was a Bravo Cat, who travelled on a barge:
In fact he was the roughest cat that ever roamed at large.
From Gravesend up to Oxford he pursued his evil aims,
Rejoicing in his title of 'The Terror of the Thames'.

His manners and appearance did not calculate to please;
His coat was torn and seedy, he was baggy at the knees;
One ear was somewhat missing, no need to tell you why,
And he scowled upon a hostile world from one forbidding eye.

The cottagers of Rotherhithe knew something of his fame;
At Hammersmith and Putney people shuddered at his name.
They would fortify the hen-house, lock up the silly goose,
Then the rumour ran along the shore: GROWLTIGER'S ON
    THE LOOSE!

Woe to the weak canary, that fluttered from its cage;
Woe to the pampered Pekinese, that faced Growltiger's rage;
Woe to the bristly Bandicoot, that lurks on foreign ships,
And woe to any Cat with whom Growltiger came to grips!

But most to Cats of foreign race his hatred had been vowed;
To Cats of foreign name and race no quarter was allowed.
The Persian and the Siamese regarded him with fear –
Because it was a Siamese had mauled his missing ear.

Now on a peaceful summer night, all nature seemed at play,
The tender moon was shining bright, the barge at Molesey lay.

All in the balmy moonlight it lay rocking on the tide –
And Growltiger was disposed to show his sentimental side.

His bucko mate, GRUMBUSKIN, long since had disappeared,
For to the Bell at Hampton he had gone to wet his beard;
And his bosun, TUMBLEBRUTUS, he too had stol'n away –
In the yard behind the Lion he was prowling for his prey.

In the forepeak of the vessel Growltiger sate alone,
Concentrating his attention on the Lady GRIDDLEBONE.
And his raffish crew were sleeping in their barrels and their
    bunks –
As the Siamese came creeping in their sampans and their junks.

Growltiger had no eye or ear for aught but Griddlebone,
And the Lady seemed enraptured by his manly baritone,
Disposed to relaxation, and awaiting no surprise –
But the moonlight shone reflected from a thousand bright
    blue eyes.

And closer still and closer the sampans circled round,
And yet from all the enemy there was not heard a sound.
The lovers sang their last duet, in danger of their lives –
For the foe was armed with toasting forks and cruel carving
      knives.

Then GILBERT gave the signal to his fierce Mongolian horde;
With a frightful burst of fireworks the Chinks they swarmed
      aboard.
Abandoning their sampans, and their pullaways and junks
They battened down the hatches on the crew within their
      bunks.

Then Griddlebone she gave a screech, for she was badly
      skeered;
I am sorry to admit it, but she quickly disappeared.
She probably escaped with ease, I'm sure she was not drowned –
But a serried ring of flashing steel Growltiger did surround.

The ruthless foe pressed forward, in stubborn rank on rank;
Growltiger to his vast surprise was forced to walk the plank.
He who a hundred victims had driven to that drop,
At the end of all his crimes was forced to go ker-flip, ker-flop.

Oh there was joy in Wapping when the news flew through the
      land;
At Maidenhead and Henley there was dancing on the strand.
Rats were roasted whole at Brentford, and at Victoria Dock,
And a day of celebration was commanded in Bangkok.

*T S Eliot*

# The fly

How large unto the tiny fly
    Must little things appear! –
A rosebud like a feather bed,
    Its prickle like a spear;

A dewdrop like a looking-glass,
    A hair like golden wire;
The smallest grain of mustard-seed
    As fierce as coals of fire;

A load of bread, a lofty hill;
    A wasp, a cruel leopard;
And specks of salt as bright to see
    As lambskins to a shepherd.

*Walter de la Mare*

# Clock a clay[1]

In the cowslips' peeps[2] I lye
Hidden from the buzzing fly
While green gras beneath me lies
Pearled wi' dew like fishes' eyes
Hiere I lie a Clock a clay
Waiting for the time o' day

[1] the ladybird. This poem is printed with the spelling and punctuation that the writer who lived in the Northamptonshire countryside in the early nineteenth century, originally used
[2] pips

While grassy forests quake surprise
And the wild wind sobs and sighs
My gold home rocks as like to fall
On its pillar green and tall
When the pattering rain drives bye
Cloack a Clay keeps warm and dry

Day by day and night by night
All the week I hide from sight
In the cowslips peeps I lie
In rain and dew still warm and dry
Day and night and night and day
Red black spotted clock a clay

My home it shakes in wind and showers
Pale green pillar topt wi' flowers
Bending at the wild winds breath
Till I touch the grass beneath
Here still I live lone clock a clay
Watching for the time of day

*John Clare*

# Hedgehog

Twitching the leaves just where the drainpipe clogs
In ivy leaves and mud, a purposeful
Creature at night about its business. Dogs
Fear his stiff seriousness. He chews away

At beetles, worms, slugs, frogs. Can kill a hen
With one snap of his jaws, can taunt a snake
To death on muscled spines. Old countrymen
Tell tales of hedgehogs sucking a cow dry.

But this one, cramped by houses, fences, walls,
Must have slept here all winter in that heap
Of compost, or have inched by intervals
Through tidy gardens to this ivy bed.

And here, dim-eyed, but ears so sensitive
A voice within the house can make him freeze,
He scuffs the edge of danger; yet can live
Happily in our nights and absences.

A country creature, wary, quiet and shrewd,
He takes the milk we give him, when we're gone.
At night, our slamming voices must seem crude
To one who sits and waits for silences.

*Anthony Thwaite*


# Song

A widow bird sate mourning for her love
    Upon a wintry bough;
The frozen wind crept on above,
    The freezing stream below.

There was no leaf upon the forest bare,
    No flower upon the ground,
And little motion in the air
    Except the mill-wheel's sound.

*P B Shelley*

# Michael's song

Because I set no snare
But leave them flying free,
All the birds of the air
Belong to me.

From the blue-tit on the sloe
To the eagle on the height,
Uncaged they come and go
For my delight.

And so the sunward way
I soar on the eagle's wings,
And in my heart all day
The blue-tit sings.

*Wilfrid Wilson Gibson*

# The snare

I hear a sudden cry of pain!
There is a rabbit in a snare:
Now I hear the cry again,
    But I cannot tell from where.

But I cannot tell from where
    He is calling out for aid!
Crying on the frightened air,
    Making everything afraid!

Making everything afraid!
    Wrinkling up his little face!
As he cries again for aid;
    And I cannot find the place!

And I cannot find the place
    Where his paw is in the snare!
Little One! Oh, Little One!
    I am searching everywhere!

*James Stephens*

# Sheep

When I was once in Baltimore,
    A man came up to me and cried,
'Come, I have eighteen hundred sheep,
    And we will sail on Tuesday's tide.

If you will sail with me, young man,
    I'll pay you fifty shillings down;
These eighteen hundred sheep I take
    From Baltimore to Glasgow town.'

He paid me fifty shillings down,
    I sailed with eighteen hundred sheep;
We soon had cleared the harbour's mouth,
    We soon were in the salt sea deep.

The first night we were out at sea
    Those sheep were quiet in their mind;
The second night they cried with fear -
    They smelt no pastures in the wind.

They sniffed, poor things, for their green fields,
    They cried so loud I could not sleep;
For fifty thousand shillings down
    I would not sail again with sheep.

*W H Davies*

# The bells of Heaven

'Twould ring the bells of Heaven
The wildest peal for years,
If Parson lost his senses
And people came to theirs,
And he and they together

Knelt down with angry prayers
For tamed and shabby tigers
And dancing dogs and bears,
And wretched, blind pit ponies,
And little hunted hares.

*Ralph Hodgson*

# To see the rabbit

We are going to see the rabbit.
We are going to see the rabbit.
Which rabbit, people say?
Which rabbit, ask the children?
Which rabbit?
The only rabbit,
The only rabbit in England,
Sitting behind a barbed-wire fence
Under the floodlights, neon lights,
Sodium lights,
Nibbling grass
On the only patch of grass
In England, in England
(Except the grass by the hoardings
Which doesn't count).
We are going to see the rabbit
And we must be there on time.

First we shall go by escalator,
Then we shall go by underground,
And then we shall go by motorway,
And then by helicopterway,
And the last ten yards we shall have to go
On foot.

And now we are going
All the way to see the rabbit,
We are nearly there,
We are longing to see it,
And so is the crowd

Which is here in thousands
With mounted policemen
And big loudspeakers
And bands and banners,
And everyone has come a long way.

But soon we shall see it
Sitting and nibbling
The blades of grass
On the only patch of grass
In – but something has gone wrong!
Why is everyone so angry,
Why is everyone jostling
And slanging and complaining?

The rabbit has gone,
Yes, the rabbit has gone.
He has actually burrowed down into the earth
And made himself a warren, under the earth,
Despite all these people,
And what shall we do?
What *can* we do?

It is all a pity, you must be disappointed,
Go home and do something else for today,
Go home again, go home for today.
For you cannot hear the rabbit, under the earth,
Remarking rather sadly to himself, by himself,
As he rests in his warren, under the earth:
'It won't be long, they are bound to come,
They are bound to come and find me, even here.'

*Alan Brownjohn*

# Bees

Down in the plain, and up on the mountain top,
All nature's boundless glory is their prey.
But when they have sipped from a hundred flowers
        and made honey,
For whom is this toil, for whom this nectar?

*Lo Yin*
*translated by Robert Kotewall and Norman L Smith*

# February – a thaw

The snow is gone from cottage tops
The thatch moss glows in brighter green
And eves in quick succession drops
Where grinning icles once hath been
Pit patting wi a pleasant noise
In tubs set by the cottage door
And ducks and geese wi happy joys
Douse in the yard pond brimming oer

The sun peeps thro the window pane
Which children mark wi laughing eye
And in the wet street steal again
To tell each other spring is nigh

And as young hope the past recalls
In playing groups will often draw
Building beside the sunny walls
Their spring-play-huts of sticks or straw

*John Clare*

# Up in the morning early

Cauld blaws the wind frae east to west,
    The drift is driving sairly;
Sae loud and shill's I hear the blast,
    I'm sure it's winter fairly.

*Up in the morning's no for me,*
*Up in the morning early;*
*When a' the hills are cover'd wi' snaw,*
*I'm sure it is winter fairly.*

The birds sit chittering in the thorn,
A' day they fare but sparely;
And lang's the night frae e'en to mourn,
I'm sure it's winter fairly.

*Robert Burns*

# Call the cows home

*Call the cows home!*
*Call the cows home!*
Louring storm clouds
Hitherward come;
East to West
Their wings are spread;
Lost in the blue
Is each heaven-high head;
They've dimmed the sun;
Turned day to night;
With a whistling wind
The woods are white;
Down streams the rain
On farm, barn, byre,
Bright green hill,
And bramble and briar,

Filling the valley
With glimmer and gloom:
*Call the cows home!*
*Call the cows home!*

*Walter de la Mare*

# The fog

I saw the fog grow thick,
    Which soon made blind my ken;
It made tall men of boys,
    And giants of tall men.

It clutched my throat, I coughed;
    Nothing was in my head
Except two heavy eyes
    Like balls of burning lead.

And when it grew so black
    That I could know no place,
 lost all judgment then,
    Of distance and of space.

The street lamps, and the lights
    Upon the halted cars,
Could either be on earth
    Or be the heavenly stars.

A man passed by me close,
    I asked my way; he said
'Come, follow me, my friend'–
    I followed where he led.

He rapped the stones in front,
    'Trust me,' he said, 'and come';
I followed like a child –
    A blind man led me home.

*W H Davies*

# Fog

The fog comes
on little cat feet.

It sits looking
over harbour and city
on silent haunches
and then moves on.

*Carl Sandburg*

# When icicles hang

When icicles hang by the wall,
    And Dick the shepherd blows his nail,
And Tom bears logs into the hall,
    And milk comes frozen home in pail,
When blood is nipped, and ways be foul,
Then nightly sings the staring owl
                Tu-whoo;
    *Tu-whit, tu-whoo – a merry note,*
*While greasy Joan doth keel[1] the pot.*

When all aloud the wind doth blow,
    And coughing drowns the parson's saw,[2]
And birds sit brooding in the snow.
    And Marian's nose looks red and raw,
When roasted crabs[3] hiss in the bowl,
Then nightly sings the staring owl,
                Tu-whoo;
    *Tu-whit, tu-whoo – a merry note,*
*While greasy Joan doth keel the pot.*

*William Shakespeare*

o cool by stirring or skimming
vise saying
rab apples

# New Year

Ring out, wild bells, to the wild sky,
    The flying cloud, the frosty light:
    The year is dying in the night;
Ring out, wild bells, and let him die.

Ring out the old, ring in the new,
    Ring, happy bells, across the snow:
    The year is going, let him go;
Ring out the false, ring in the true.

*Lord Tennyson*

# The six blind men

It was six men of Hindostan,
    To learning much inclined,
Who went to see the Elephant
    (Though all of them were blind),
That each by observation
    Might satisfy his mind.

The *First* approached the Elephant,
    And happening to fall
Against his broad and sturdy side,
    At once began to bawl:
Bless me, it seems the Elephant
    Is very like a wall!'

The *Second*, feeling of the tusk,
    Cried, 'Ho! what have we here
So very round and smooth and sharp?
    To me 'tis mighty clear
This wonder of an Elephant
    Is very like a spear!'

The *Third* approached the animal,
    And happening to take
The squirming trunk within his hands,
    Then boldly up and spake:
I see,' quoth he, 'the Elephant
    Is very like a snake!'

The *Fourth* stretched out his eager hand
    And felt about the knee,
'What most this mighty beast is like
    Is mighty plain,' quoth he;
''Tis clear enough the Elephant
    Is very like a tree!'

The *Fifth*, who chanced to touch the ear,
    Said, 'E'en the blindest man
Can tell what this resembles most;
    Deny the fact who can,
This marvel of an Elephant
    Is very like a fan!'

The *Sixth* no sooner had begun
    About the beast to grope,
Than, seizing on the swinging tail
    That fell within his scope,
'I see,' said he, 'the Elephant
    Is very like a rope!'

And so these men of Hindostan
    Disputed loud and long,
Each in his own opinion
    Exceeding stiff and strong,
Though each was partly in the right,
    And all were in the wrong!

*John G Saxe*

# Tony the Turtle

Tony was a Turtle,
    Very much at ease,
Swimming in the sunshine
    Through the summer seas,
And feeding on the fishes
Irrespective of their wishes,
With a 'By your leave' and 'Thank you'
    And a gentlemanly squeeze.

Tony was a Turtle
    Who loved a civil phrase;
Anxious and obliging,
    Sensitive to praise.
And to hint that he was snappy
Made him thoroughly unhappy;
For Tony was a Turtle
    With most engaging ways.

Tony was a Turtle
    Who thought, before he fed,
Of other people's comfort,
    And as he ate them said:
'If I seem a little grumpy,
It is *not* that you are lumpy.'
For Tony was a Turtle
    Delicately bred.

*E V Rieu*

# Matilda

*who told lies, and was burned to death*

Matilda told such Dreadful Lies,
It made one Gasp and Stretch one's Eyes;
Her Aunt, who, from her Earliest Youth,
Had kept a Strict Regard for Truth,
Attempted to Believe Matilda:
The effort very nearly killed her,
And would have done so, had not She
Discovered this Infirmity.

For once, towards the Close of Day,
Matilda, growing tired of play,
And finding she was left alone,
Went tiptoe to the Telephone,
And summoned the Immediate Aid
Of London's Noble Fire-Brigade.

Within an hour the Gallant Band
Were pouring in on every hand,
From Putney, Hackney Downs, and Bow
With Courage high and Hearts a-glow
They galloped, roaring through the Town,
'Matilda's House is Burning Down!'
Inspired by British Cheers and Loud
Proceeding from the Frenzied Crowd,
They ran their ladders through a score
Of windows on the Ball Room floor;
And took Peculiar Pains to Souse
The Pictures up and down the House,

Until Matilda's aunt succeeded
In showing them they were not needed;
And even then she had to pay
To get the Men to go away!

.    .    .    .    .

It happened that a few Weeks later,
Her aunt was off to the Theatre,
To see that Interesting Play,
*The Second Mrs. Tanqueray*.
She had refused to take her Niece
To hear this Entertaining Piece:
A Deprivation Just and Wise,
To Punish her for Telling Lies.

That Night a Fire *did* break out –
You should have heard Matilda Shout!
You should have heard her Scream and Bawl,
And throw the window up and call
To People passing in the street –
(The rapidly increasing Heat
Encouraging her to obtain
Their confidence) – but all in vain!
For every time She shouted 'Fire!'
They only answered 'Little Liar!'
And therefore when her aunt returned,
Matilda, and the House, were Burned.

*Hilaire Belloc*

# Shut the door

Godfrey Gordon Gustavus Gore –
No doubt you've heard the name before –
Was a boy who never would shut a door!

The wind might whistle, the wind might roar,
And teeth be aching, and throats be sore,
But still he never would shut the door.

His father would beg, his mother implore,
'Godfrey Gordon Gustavus Gore,
We really *do* wish you would shut the door!'

They rigged out a shutter with sail and oar,
And threatened to pack off Gustavus Gore
On a voyage of penance to Singapore.

But he begged for mercy, and said, 'No more!
Pray do not send me to Singapore
On a shutter, and then I will shut the door!'

'You will?' said his parents. 'Then keep on shore;
But mind you do! For the plague is sore
Of a fellow that never will shut the door –
Godfrey Gordon Gustavus Gore!'

*William Brighty Rands*

# The cataract of Lodore

'How does the Water
Come down at Lodore?'

My little boy ask'd me
Thus, once on a time;
And moreover he task'd me
To tell him in rhyme.

Anon at the word,
There came first one daughter
And then came another,
To second and third
The request of their brother,
And to hear how the water
Comes down at Lodore,
With its rush and its roar,
As many a time
They had seen it before.
So I told them in rhyme,
For of rhymes I had store:
And 'twas in my vocation
For their recreation
That so I should sing;
Because I was Laureate
To them and the King.
From its sources which well
In the Tarn on the fell;

From its fountains
In the mountains,
Its rills and its gills;
Through moss and through brake,
It runs and it creeps
For a while, till it sleeps
In its own little Lake,
And thence at departing
Awakening and starting,
It runs through the reeds,
And away it proceeds,
Through meadow and glade,
In sun and in shade,
And through the wood-shelter,
Among crags in its flurry,
Helter-skelter,
Hurry-scurry.
Here it comes sparkling,
And there it lies darkling;
Now smoking and frothing
Its tumult and wrath in,
Till in this rapid race
On which it is bent,
It reaches the place
Of its steep descent.

The cataract strong
Then plunges along,
Striking and raging
As if a war waging
Its caverns and rocks among:

Rising and leaping,
Sinking and creeping,
Swelling and sweeping,
Showering and springing,
Flying and flinging,
Writhing and ringing,
Eddying and whisking,
Spouting and frisking,
Twining and twisting,
    Around and around
    With endless rebound!
Smiting and fighting,
A sight to delight in:
Confounding, astounding,
Dizzying and deafening the ear with its sound.

Collecting, projecting,
Receding and speeding,
And shocking and rocking,
And darting and parting,
And threading and spreading,
And whizzing and hissing,
And dripping and skipping,
And hitting and splitting,
And shining and twining,
And rattling and battling,
And shaking and quaking,
And pouring and roaring,
And waving and raving,
And tossing and crossing,
And flowing and going,
And running and stunning,

And foaming and roaming,
And dinning and spinning
And dropping and hopping,
And working and jerking,
And guggling and struggling,
And heaving and cleaving,
And moaning and groaning;

And glittering and frittering,
And gathering and feathering,
And whitening and brightening,
And quivering and shivering,
And hurrying and skurrying,
And thundering and floundering;

Dividing and gliding and sliding,
And falling and crawling and sprawling,
And driving and riving and striving,
And sprinkling and twinkling and wrinkling,
And sounding and bounding and rounding,
And bubbling and troubling and doubling,
And grumbling and rumbling and tumbling,
And clattering and battering and shattering;

Retreating and beating and meeting and sheeting,
Delaying and straying and playing and spraying,
Advancing and prancing and glancing and dancing,
Recoiling, turmoiling and toiling and boiling,
And gleaming and steaming and streaming and beaming,
And rushing and flushing and brushing and gushing,
And flapping and rapping and clapping and slapping,
And curling and whirling and purling and twirling,
And thumping and plumping and bumping and jumping,

And dashing and flashing and splashing and clashing;
And so never ending, but always descending,
Sounds and motions for ever and ever are blending,
All at once and all o'er, with a mighty uproar,
And this way the Water comes down at Lodore.

*Robert Southey*

# The little brother

God! how they plague his life, the three damned sisters,
Throwing stones at him out of the cherry trees,
Pulling his hair, smudging his exercises,
Whispering. How passionately he sees
His spilt minnows flounder in the grass.

There will be sisters subtler far than these,
Baleful and dark, with slender, cared-for hands,
Who will not smirk and babble in the trees,
But feed him with sweet words and provocations,
And in his sleep practise their sorceries,
Appearing in the form of ragged clouds
And at the corners of malignant seas.

As with his wounded life he goes alone
To the world's end, where even tears freeze,
He will in bitter memory and remorse
Hear the lost sisters innocently tease.

*James Reeves*

# My sister Jane

And I say nothing, – no, not a word
About our Jane. Haven't you heard?
She's a bird, a bird, a bird, a bird.
Oh it never would do to let folks know
My sister's nothing but a great big crow.

Each day (we daren't send her to school)
She pulls on stockings of thick blue wool
To make her pin crow legs look right,
Then fits a wig of curls on tight,
And dark spectacles – a huge pair
To cover her very crowy stare.
Oh it never would do to let folks know
My sister's nothing but a great big crow.

When visitors come she sits upright
(With her wings and her tail tucked out of sight).
They think her queer but extremely polite.
Then when the visitors have gone
She whips out her wings and with her wig on
Whirls through the house at the height of your head –
Duck, duck, or she'll knock you dead.
Oh it never would do to let folks know
My sister's nothing but a great big crow.

At meals whatever she sees she'll stab it –
Because she's a crow and that's a crow habit.
My mother says 'Jane! Your manners! Please!'
Then she'll sit quietly on the cheese,
Or play the piano nicely by dancing on the keys –
Oh it never would do to let folks know
My sister's nothing but a great big crow.

*Ted Hughes*

# The twins

In form and feature, face and limb,
　　I grew so like my brother,
That folks got taking me for him,
　　And each for one another.
It puzzled all our kith and kin,
　　It reached a fearful pitch,
For one of us was born a twin,
　　Yet not a soul knew which.

One day (to make the matter worse),
　　Before our names were fixed,
As we were being washed by nurse,
　　We got completely mixed;
And thus you see, by Fate's decree,
　　(Or rather nurse's whim),
My brother John got christened *me*,
　　And I got christened *him*.

This fatal likeness even dogged
　　My footsteps when at school,
And I was always getting flogged,
　　For John turned out a fool.
I put this question hopelessly
　　To everyone I knew,
'What *would* you do, if you were me,
　　To prove that you were *you*?'

Our close resemblance turned the tide
    Of my domestic life;
For somehow my intended bride
    Became my brother's wife.
In short, year after year, the same
    Absurd mistakes went on;
And when I died – the neighbours came
    And buried brother John!

*H S Leigh*

# Brother

It's odd enough to be alive with others,
But odder still to have sisters and brothers;
To make one of a characteristic litter –
The sisters puzzled and vexed, the brothers vexed and bitter
That this one wears, though flattened by abuse,
The family nose for individual use.

*Robert Graves*

# The village boy

Free from the cottage corner see how wild
The village boys along the pasture hies
With every smell and sound and sight beguiled
That round the prospect meets his wondering eyes
Now stooping eager for the cowslip peeps
As though hed get them all – now tired of these
Across the flaggy brook he eager leaps
For some new flower his happy rapture sees
Now tearing mid the bushes on his knees
On woodland banks for blue bell flowers he creeps
And now while looking up among the trees
He spies a nest and down he throws his flowers
And up he climbs with new fed extacies
The happiest object in the summer hours

*John Clare*

# The chimney sweeper

A little black thing among the snow,
Crying ''weep! 'weep!' in notes of woe!
'Where are thy father & mother? say?'
'They are both gone up to the church to pray.

'Because I was happy upon the heath,
'And smil'd among the winter's snow,
'They clothed me in the clothes of death,
'And taught me to sing the notes of woe.

'And because I am happy & dance & sing,
'They think they have done me no injury,
'And are gone to praise God & his Priest & King,
'Who make up a heaven of our misery.'

*William Blake*

# Fourpence a day

The ore's[1] awaitin' in the tubs; the snow's upon the fell.
Canny folk are sleepin' yet but lead is reet[2] to sell.
Come my little washer lad, come, let's away.
We're bound down to slavery for fourpence a day.

It's early in the morning; we rise at five o'clock
And the little slaves come to the door to knock, knock, knock
Come my little washer lad, come, let's away,
It's very hard to work for fourpence a day.

My father was a miner; he lived down in the town,
'Twas hard work and poverty that always kept him down.
He aimed for us to go to school, but brass he couldn't pay,
So we had to go to the washing rake for fourpence a day.

Fourpence a day, my lad, and very hard to work,
And never a pleasant word from a gruffy lookin' 'Turk'.
His conscience it may fail and his heart it may give way,
Then he's raise us our wages to ninepence a day.

*Unknown nineteenth-century author*

[1] lead ore, which is mined by the father singing this song
[2] ready

# The fisherman's apprentice

*Around* 1800 *the cruel fisherman Peter Grimes buys an orphaned boy, called Sam, from the parish workhouse to help him with his fishing off the coast of Suffolk.*

     Peter had heard there were in London then, –
Still have they being! – workhouse[1]-clearing men,
Who, undisturb'd by feelings just or kind,
Would parish-boys to needy tradesmen bind[2]:
They in their want a trifling sum would take,
And toiling slaves of piteous orphans make.

     Such Peter sought, and when a lad was found,
The sum was dealt him, and the slave was bound.
Some few in town observed in Peter's trap[3]
A boy, with jacket blue and woollen cap;
But none enquired how Peter used the rope,
Or what the bruise, that made the stripling stoop;
None could the ridges on his back behold,
None sought him shiv'ring in the winter's cold;
None put the question, – 'Peter, dost thou give
'The boy his food? – What, man! the lad must live:
'Consider, Peter, let the child have bread,
'He'll serve thee better if he's stroked and fed.'
None reason'd thus – and some, on hearing cries,
Said calmly, 'Grimes is at his exercise.'

[1] where the poor or homeless were made to work
[2] legally tied to a master as an apprentice
[3] cart

Pinn'd, beaten, cold, pinch'd, threaten'd, and abused –
His efforts punish'd and his food refused, –
Awake tormented, – soon aroused from sleep, –
Struck if he wept, and yet compell'd to weep,
The trembling boy dropp'd down and strove to pray,
Received a blow, and trembling turn'd away,
Or sobb'd and hid his piteous face; – while he,
The savage master, grinn'd in horrid glee:
He'd now the power he ever loved to show,
A feeling[4] being subject to his blow.

Thus lived the lad, in hunger, peril, pain,
His tears despised, his supplications vain[5]:
Compell'd by fear to lie, by need to steal,
His bed uneasy and unbless'd his meal,
For three sad years the boy his tortures bore,
And then his pains and trials were no more.

'How died he, Peter?' when the people said,
He growl'd – 'I found him lifeless in his bed;'
Then tried for softer tone, and sigh'd, 'Poor Sam is dead.'
Yet murmurs were there, and some questions ask'd –
How he was fed, how punish'd, and how task'd?
Much they suspected, but they little proved,
And Peter pass'd untroubled and unmoved.

*George Crabbe*
*from 'Peter Grimes'*

sensitive
pleadings ignored

# The schoolboy

I love to rise in a summer morn
When the birds sing on every tree;
The distant huntsman winds his horn,
And the sky-lark sings with me.
O! what sweet company.

But to go to school in a summer morn,
O! it drives all joy away;
Under a cruel eye outworn,
The little ones spend the day
In sighing and dismay.

Ah! then at times I drooping sit,
And spend many an anxious hour,
Nor in my book can I take delight,
Nor sit in learning's bower
Worn through with the dreary shower.

How can the bird that is born for joy
Sit in a cage and sing?
How can a child, when fears annoy,
But droop his tender wing
And forget his youthful spring?

O! father and mother, if buds are nipped
And blossoms blown away,
And if the tender plants are stripped
Of their joy in the springing day,
By sorrow and care's dismay,

How shall the summer arise in joy,
Or the summer fruits appear?
Or how shall we gather what griefs destroy,
Or bless the mellowing year,
When the blasts of winter appear?

*William Blake*

# The place's fault

Once, after a rotten day at school –
Sweat on my fingers, pages thumbed with smears,
Cane smashing down to make me keep them neat –
I blinked out to the sunlight and the heat
And stumbled up the hill, still swallowing tears.
A stone hissed past my ear – 'yah! gurt fat fool!'

Some urchins waited for me by my gate.
I shouted swear-words at them, walked away.
'Yeller', they yelled, ''e's yeller!' And they flung
Clods, stones, bricks – anything to make me run.
I ran, all right, up hill all scorching day,
With 'yeller' in my ears. 'I'm not, I'm not!'

Another time, playing too near the shops –
Oddly no doubt, I'm told I was quite odd,
Making, no doubt, a noise – a girl in slacks
Came out and told some kids 'Run round the back,
Bash in his back door, smash up his back yard,
And if he yells I'll go and fetch the cops.'

And what a rush I had to lock those doors
Before the rabble reached them! What desire
I've had these twenty years to lock away
That place where fingers pointed out my play,
Where even the grass was tangled with barbed wire,
Where through the streets I waged continual wars!

We left (it was a temporary halt)
The knots of ragged kids, the wired-off beach,
Faces behind the blinds. I'll not return;
There's nothing there I haven't had to learn,
And I've learned nothing that I'd care to teach –
Except that I know it was the place's fault.

*Philip Hobsbaum*

# The rescue

The boy climbed up into the tree.
The tree rocked. So did he.
He was trying to rescue a cat,
A cushion of a cat, from where it sat
In a high crutch of branches, mewing
As though to say to him, 'Nothing doing,'
Whenever he shouted, 'Come on, come down.'
So up he climbed, and the whole town
Lay at his feet, round him the leaves
Fluttered like a lady's sleeves,
And the cat sat, and the wind blew so
That he would have flown had he let go.

At last he was high enough to scoop
That fat white cushion or nincompoop
And tuck her under his arm and turn
To go down –
     But oh! he began to learn
How high he was, how hard it would be,
Having come up with four limbs, to go down with three.
His heart-beats knocked as he tried to think:
He would put the cat in a lower chink –
She appealed to him with a cry of alarm
And put her eighteen claws in his arm.
So he stayed looking down for a minute or so,
To the good ground so far below.
When the minute began he saw it was hard;
When it ended he couldn't move a yard.
So there he was stuck, in the failing light
And the wind rising with the coming of the night.

His father! He shouted for all he was worth.
His father came nearer: 'What on earth – ?'

'I've got the cat up here but I'm stuck.'
'Hold on . . . ladder . . .', he heard. O luck!
How lovely behind the branches tossing
The globes at the pedestrian crossing
And the big fluorescent lamps glowed
Mauve-green on the main road.
But his father didn't come back, didn't come;
His little fingers were going numb.
The cat licked them as though to say
Are you feeling cold? I'm O.K.'

He wanted to cry, he would count ten first,
But just as he was ready to burst
A torch came and his father and mother
And a ladder and the dog and his younger brother.
Up on a big branch stood his father,
His mother came to the top of the ladder,
His brother stood on a lower rung,
The dog sat still and put out its tongue
From one to the other the cat was handed
And afterwards she was reprimanded.
After that it was easy, though the wind blew:
The parents came down, the boy came too
From the ladder, the lower branch and the upper
And all of them went indoors to supper,
And the tree rocked, and the moon sat
In the high branches like a white cat.

*Hal Summers*

# The boy in the barn

A little boy wandering alone in the night
Went in a barn all wrecked and decayed;
And the bats and the moths and the fluttering things
Flew in his face and made him afraid.

So he fell on the floor and buried his head,
And his lantern fell down at his feet;
And he heard as he lay on the sweet-smelling hay
His little heart beat, beat, beat . . .

O little boy lift your light aloft
And the bats will scamper away;
And the big brown moths will kiss the flame
And flutter down dead on the sweet-smelling hay.

*Herbert Read*

# Travel

I should like to rise and go
Where the golden apples grow; –
Where below another sky
Parrot islands anchored lie,
And, watched by cockatoos and goats,
Lonely Crusoes building boats; –

Where in sunshine reaching out
Eastern cities, miles about,
Are with mosque and minaret
Among sandy gardens set,
And the rich goods from near and far
Hang for sale in the bazaar; –

Where the Great Wall round China goes,
And on one side the desert blows,
And with bell and voice and drum,
Cities on the other hum; –

Where are forests, hot as fire,
Wide as England, tall as a spire,
Full of apes and coco-nuts
And the negro hunters' huts; –

Where the knotty crocodile
Lies and blinks in the Nile,
And the red flamingo flies
Hunting fish before his eyes; –

Where in jungles, near and far,
Man-devouring tigers are,
Lying close and giving ear
Lest the hunt be drawing near,
Or a comer-by be seen
Swinging in a palanquin; –

Where among the desert sands
Some deserted city stands,
All its children, sweep and prince,
Grown to manhood ages since,
Not a foot in street or house,
Not a stir of child or mouse,
And when kindly falls the night,
In all the town no spark of light.

There I'll come when I'm a man
With a camel caravan;
Light a fire in the gloom
Of some dusty dining-room;
See the pictures on the walls,
Heroes, fights and festivals;
And in the corner find the toys
Of the old Egyptian boys.

*Robert Louis Stevenson*

# Robin Hood and the friars

Bold Robin has robed him in ghostly attire,
And forth he is gone like a holy friar,
    *Singing, hey down, ho down, down, derry down:*
And of two grey friars he soon was aware,
Regaling themselves with dainty fare,
    *All on the fallen leaves so brown.*

'Good morrow, good brothers,' said bold Robin Hood,
'And what make you in good greenwood,
    *Singing, hey down, ho down, down, derry down!*
Now give me, I pray you, wine and food;
For none can I find in the good greenwood,
    *All on the fallen leaves so brown.'*

'Good brother,' they said, 'we would give you full fain,
 But we have no more than enough for twain,
    *Singing, hey down, ho down, down, derry down.'*
'Then give me some money,' said bold Robin Hood,
'For none can I find in the good greenwood,
    *All on the fallen leaves so brown.'*

'No money have we, good brother,' said they:
'Then,' said he, 'we three for money will pray,
    *Singing, hey down, ho down, down, derry down:*
And whatever shall come at the end of our prayer,
We three holy friars will piously share,
    *All on the fallen leaves so brown.'*

We will not pray with thee, good brother, God wot;
For truly, good brother, thou pleasest us not,
    *Singing, hey down, ho down, down, derry down.'*
Then up they both started from Robin to run,
But down on their knees Robin pulled them each one,
    *All on the fallen leaves so brown.*

The grey friars prayed with a doleful face
But bold Robin prayed with a right merry grace,
    *Singing, hey down, ho down, down, derry down:*
And when they had prayed their portmanteau he took,
And from it a hundred good angels[1] he shook
    *All on the fallen leaves so brown.*

'The saints,' said bold Robin, 'have hearkened our prayer,
And here's a good angel apiece for your share;
If more you would have, you must win ere you wear,
    *Singing, hey down, ho down, down, derry down.'*
Then he blew his good horn with a musical cheer,
And fifty good bowmen came trooping full near,
And away the grey friars they bounded like deer,
    *All on the fallen leaves so brown.*

*Thomas Love Peacock*

old English gold coins

# Robin Hood and the bishop

Come, gentlemen all, and listen a while;
    And a story I'll to you unfold –
How Robin Hood served the Bishop,
    When he robbed him of his gold.

As it befell in merry Barnsdale,
    And under the green-wood tree,
The Bishop of Hereford was to come by,
    With all his company.

'Come, kill a ven'son,' said bold Robin Hood,
    'Come kill me a good fat deer;
The Bishop's to dine with me today,
    And he shall pay well for his cheer.'

'We'll kill a fat ven'son,' said bold Robin Hood,
    'And dress't by the highway-side,
And narrowly watch for the Bishop,
    Lest some other way he should ride.'

He dressed himself up in shepherd's attire,
    With six of his men also;
And the Bishop of Hereford came thereby,
    As about the fire they did go.

'What matter is this?' said the Bishop;
    'Or for whom do you make this ado?
Or why do you kill the King's ven'son,
    When your company is so few?'

'We are shepherds,' said bold Robin Hood,
    'And we keep sheep all the year;
And we are disposed to be merry this day,
    And to kill of the King's fat deer.'

'You are brave fellows,' said the Bishop,
    'And the King of your doings shall know;
Therefore make haste, and come along with me,
    For before the King you shall go.'

'O pardon, O pardon,' said bold Robin Hood,
    'O pardon, I thee pray!
For it never becomes your lordship's coat
    To take so many lives away.'

'No pardon, no pardon!' the Bishop says,
    'No pardon I thee owe;
Therefore make haste, come along with me,
    For before the King you shall go.'

Robin set his back against a tree,
    And his foot against a thorn,
And from underneath his shepherd's coat
    He pulled out a bugle horn.

He put the little end to his mouth,
    And a loud blast did he blow,
Till three score and ten of bold Robin's men
    Came running all on a row;

All making obeisance to bold Robin Hood;
    –'Twas a comely sight for to see:
'What matter, my master,' said Little John,
    'That you blow so hastily?'–

'O here is the Bishop of Hereford,
    And no pardon we shall have':–
'Cut off his head, master,' said Little John,
    'And throw him into his grave.'

'O pardon, O pardon,' said the Bishop,
    'O pardon, I thee pray!
For if I had known it had been you,
    I'd have gone some other way.'

'No pardon, no pardon!' said Robin Hood,
    'No pardon I thee owe;
Therefore make haste, and come along with me,
    For to merry Barnsdale you shall go.'

Then Robin he took the Bishop's hand,
    And led him to merry Barnsdale;
He made him to stay and sup with him that night,
    And to drink wine, beer and ale.

'Call in the reckoning,' said the Bishop,
    'For methinks it grows wondrous high.'–
'Lend me your purse, Bishop,' said Little John,
    'And I'll tell you by and by.'

Then Little John took the Bishop's cloak,
    And spread it upon the ground,
And out of the Bishop's portmanteau
    He told three hundred pound.

'So now let him go,' said Robin Hood;
    Said Little John, 'That may not be;
For I vow and protest he shall sing us a mass,
    Before that he go from me.'

Robin Hood took the Bishop by the hand,
    And bound him fast to a tree,
And made him to sing a mass, God wot,
    To him and his yeomanry.

Then Robin Hood brought him through the wood
    And caused the music to play,
And he made the Bishop to dance in his boots,
    And they set him on 's dapple-grey,
And they gave him the tail within his hand –
    And glad he could so get away!

*Not known*

# The highwayman

The wind was a torrent of darkness
    among the gusty trees,
The moon was a ghostly galleon
    tossed upon cloudy seas,
The road was a ribbon of moonlight
    over the purple moor,
And the highwayman came riding –
    Riding – Riding –
The highwayman came riding,
    up to the old inn-door.

He'd a French cocked-hat on his forehead,
    a bunch of lace at his chin,
A coat of the claret velvet,
    and breeches of brown doe-skin;
They fitted with never a wrinkle:
    His boots were up to the thigh!
And he rode with a jewelled twinkle,
    His pistol butts a-twinkle,
His rapier hilt a-twinkle,
    under the jewelled sky.

Over the cobbles he clattered
    and clashed in the dark inn-yard,
And he tapped with his whip on the shutters,
    but all was locked and barred;
He whistled a tune to the window,
    and who should be waiting there
But the landlord's black-eyed daughter,
    Bess, the landlord's daughter,
Plaiting a dark red love-knot into her long black hair.

And dark in the dark old inn-yard
      a stable-wicket creaked
Where Tim the ostler listened.
      His face was white and peaked;
His eyes were hollows of madness,
      his hair like mouldy hay,
But he loved the landlord's daughter,
      The landlord's red-lipped daughter,
Dumb as a dog he listened, and he heard the robber say –

'One kiss, my bonny sweetheart,
      I'm after a prize tonight,
But I shall be back with the yellow gold
      before the morning light;
Yet, if they press me sharply,
      and harry me through the day,
Then look for me by moonlight,
      Watch for me by moonlight,
I'll come to thee by moonlight,
      though hell should bar the way.'

He rose upright in the stirrups;
      he scarce could reach her hand,
But she loosened her hair i' the casement!
      His face burnt like a brand
As the black cascade of perfume
      came tumbling over his breast;
And he kissed its waves in the moonlight,
      (Oh, sweet black waves in the moonlight!)
Then he tugged at his rein in the moonlight,
      and galloped away to the West.

He did not come in the dawning;
    he did not come at noon;
And out o' the tawny sunset,
    before the rise o' the moon,
When the road was a gipsy's ribbon,
    looping the purple moor,
A red-coat troop came marching –
    Marching – marching –
King George's men came marching,
    up to the old inn-door.

They said no word to the landlord,
    they drank his ale instead,
But they gagged his daughter and bound her
    to the foot of her narrow bed.
Two of them knelt at her casement,
    with muskets at their side!
There was death at every window;
    And hell at one dark window;
For Bess could see, through her casement,
    the road that *he* would ride.

They had tied her up to attention,
    with many a sniggering jest;
They had bound a musket beside her,
    with the muzzle beneath her breast!
'Now, keep good watch!' and they kissed her.
    She heard the dead man say –
*Look for me by moonlight;*
    *Watch for me by moonlight;*
*I'll come to thee by moonlight,*
    *though hell should bar the way!*

She twisted her hands behind her;
    but all the knots held good!
She writhed her hands till her fingers
    were wet with sweat or blood!
They stretched and strained in the darkness,
    and the hours crawled by like years,
Till, now, on the stroke of midnight,
    Cold, on the stroke of midnight,
The tip of one finger touched it!
    The trigger at least was hers!

The tip of one finger touched it.
    She strove no more for the rest!
Up, she stood up to attention,
    with the muzzle beneath her breast.
She would not risk their hearing;
    she would not strive again;
For the road lay bare in the moonlight;
    Blank and bare in the moonlight;
And the blood of her veins, in the moonlight,
    throbbed to her love's refrain.

*Tlot-tlot; tlot-tlot!* Had they heard it?
    The horsehoofs ringing clear;
*Tlot-tlot, tlot-tlot*, in the distance?
    Were they deaf that they did not hear?
Down the ribbon of moonlight,
    over the brow of the hill,
The highwayman came riding,
    Riding, riding!
The red-coats looked to their priming!
    She stood up, straight and still.

*Tlot-tlot*, in the frosty silence!
    *Tlot-tlot,* in the echoing night!
Nearer he came and nearer!
    Her face was like a light!
Her eyes grew wide for a moment;
    she drew one last deep breath,
Then her finger moved in the moonlight,
    Her musket shattered the moonlight,
Shattered her breast in the moonlight
    and warned him – with her death.

He turned; he spurred to the westward;
    he did not know who stood
Bowed, with her head o'er the musket,
    drenched with her own blood!
Not till the dawn he heard it,
    and slowly blanched to hear
How Bess, the landlord's daughter,
    The landlord's black-eyed daughter,
Had watched for her love in the moonlight,
    and died in the darkness there.

Back, he spurred like a madman,
    shrieking a curse to the sky,
With the white road smoking behind him
    and his rapier brandished high!
Blood-red were his spurs i' the golden noon;
    wine-red was his velvet coat;
When they shot him down on the highway,
    Down like a dog on the highway,
And he lay in his blood on the highway,
    with the bunch of lace at his throat.

      .     .     .

*And still of a winter's night, they say,*
      *when the wind is in the trees,*
*When the moon is a ghostly galleon*
      *tossed upon cloudy seas,*
*When the road is a ribbon of moonlight*
      *over the purple moor,*
*A highwayman comes riding –*
      *Riding – riding –*
*A highwayman comes riding, up to the old inn-door.*

*Over the cobbles he clatters and clangs*
      *in the dark inn-yard;*
*He taps with his whip on the shutters,*
      *but all is locked and barred;*
*He whistles a tune to the window,*
      *and who should be waiting there*
*But the landlord's black-eyed daughter,*
      *Bess, the landlord's daughter,*
*Plaiting a dark red love-knot into her long black hair.*

*Alfred Noyes*

# A smuggler's song

If you wake at midnight and hear a horse's feet,
Don't go drawing back the blind, or looking in the street,
Them that asks no questions isn't told a lie.
Watch the wall, my darling, while the Gentlemen go by!
     Five and twenty ponies,
     Trotting through the dark –
     Brandy for the Parson,
     'Baccy for the Clerk;
     Laces for a lady; letters for a spy,
And watch the wall, my darling, while the Gentlemen go by!

Running round the woodlump if you chance to find
Little barrels, roped and tarred, all full of brandy-wine,
Don't you shout to come and look, nor take 'em for your play.
Put the brushwood back again, – and they'll be gone next day!

If you see the stableyard setting open wide;
If you see a tired horse lying down inside;
If your mother mends a coat cut about and tore;
If the lining's wet and warm – don't you ask no more!

If you meet King George's men, dressed in blue and red,
You be careful what you say, and mindful what is said.
If they call you 'pretty maid', and chuck you 'neath the chin,
Don't you tell where no one is, nor yet where no one's been!

Knocks and footsteps round the house – whistles after dark –
You've no call for running out till the house-dogs bark.
*Trusty's* here and *Pincher's* here, and see how dumb they lie –
*They* don't fret to follow when the Gentlemen go by!

If you do as you've been told, 'likely there's a chance,
You'll be give a dainty doll, all the way from France,
With a cap of Valenciennes, and a velvet hood –
A present from the Gentlemen, along o' being good!
    Five and twenty ponies,
     Trotting through the dark –
     Brandy for the Parson,
     'Baccy for the Clerk.
Them that asks no questions isn't told a lie –
Watch the wall, my darling, while the Gentlemen go by!

*Rudyard Kipling*

# O what is that sound which so thrills the ear

O what is that sound which so thrills the ear
    Down in the valley drumming, drumming?
Only the scarlet soldiers, dear,
    The soldiers coming.

O what is that light I see flashing so clear
    Over the distance brightly, brightly?
Only the sun on their weapons, dear,
    As they step lightly.

O what are they doing with all that gear,
    What are they doing this morning, this morning?
Only their usual manœuvres, dear,
    Or perhaps a warning.

O why have they left the road down there,
    Why are they suddenly wheeling, wheeling?
Perhaps a change in their orders, dear,
    Why are you kneeling?

O haven't they stopped for the doctor's care,
    Haven't they reined their horses, their horses?
Why, they are none of them wounded, dear,
    None of these forces.

O is it the parson they want, with white hair,
    Is it the parson, is it, is it?
No, they are passing his gateway, dear,
    Without a visit.

O it must be the farmer who lives so near.
    It must be the farmer so cunning, so cunning?
They have passed the farmyard already, dear,
    And now they are running.

O where are you going? Stay with me here!
    Were the vows you swore deceiving, deceiving?
No, I promised to love you, dear,
    But I must be leaving.

O it's broken the lock and splintered the door,
    O it's the gate where they're turning, turning;
Their boots are heavy on the floor
    And their eyes are burning.

*W H Auden*

# The Inchcape Rock

No stir in the air, no stir in the sea,
The ship was still as she could be,
Her sails from heaven received no motion,
Her keel was steady in the ocean.

Without either sign or sound of their shock
The waves flowed over the Inchcape Rock;
So little they rose, so little they fell,
They did not move the Inchcape Bell.

The worthy Abbot of Aberbrothok
Had placed that bell on the Inchcape Rock;
On a buoy in the storm it floated and swung,
And over the waves its warning rung.

When the Rock was hid by the surge's swell,
The mariners heard the warning bell;
And then they knew the perilous rock
And blessed the Abbot of Aberbrothok.

The sun in heaven was shining gay,
All things were joyful on that day;
The sea-birds screamed as they wheeled round,
And there was joyaunce in their sound.

The buoy of the Inchcape Bell was seen,
A darker speck on the ocean green;
Sir Ralph the Rover walked his deck,
And he fixed his eye on the darker speck.

He felt the cheering power of spring;
It made him whistle, it made him sing;
His heart was mirthful to excess,
But the Rover's mirth was wickedness.

His eye was on the Inchcape float;
Quoth he, 'My men, put out the boat,
And row me to the Inchcape Rock,
And I'll plague the Abbot of Aberbrothok.'

The boat is lowered, the boatmen row,
And to the Inchcape Rock they go;
Sir Ralph bent over from the boat,
And he cut the Bell from the Inchcape float.

Down sunk the Bell with a gurgling sound,
The bubbles arose and burst around;
Quoth Sir Ralph, 'The next who comes to the Rock
Won't bless the Abbot of Aberbrothok.'

Sir Ralph the Rover sailed away,
He scoured the seas for many a day;
And now grown rich with plundered store,
He steers his course for Scotland's shore.

So thick a haze o'erspreads the sky
They cannot see the sun on high;
The wind hath blown a gale all day,
At evening it hath died away.

On the deck the Rover takes his stand,
So dark it is they see no land.
Quoth Sir Ralph, 'It will be lighter soon,
For there is the dawn of the rising Moon.'

Canst hear,' said one, 'the breakers roar?
For methinks we should be near the shore.'
Now where we are I cannot tell,
But I wish I could hear the Inchcape Bell.'

They hear no sound, the swell is strong;
Though the wind hath fallen, they drift along,
Till the vessel strikes with a shivering shock, –
O Christ! it is the Inchcape Rock!'

Sir Ralph the Rover tore his hair;
He cursed himself in his despair;
But the waves rush in on every side,
And the vessel sinks beneath the tide.

*Robert Southey*

# Barbara Frietchie

Up from the meadows rich with corn,
Clear in the cool September morn,
The clustered spires of Frederick stand
Green-walled by the hills of Maryland.
Round about them orchards sweep,
Apple and peach tree fruited deep,
Fair as the garden of the Lord

To the eyes of the famished rebel horde,
On that pleasant morn of the early fall
When Lee marched over the mountain-wall,
Over the mountains winding down,
Horse and foot, into Frederick town.
Forty flags with their silver stars,
Forty flags with their crimson bars,
Flapped in the morning wind: the sun
Of noon looked down, and saw not one.

Up rose old Barbara Frietchie then,
Bowed with her fourscore years and ten;
Bravest of all in Frederick town,
She took up the flag the men hauled down;
In her attic window the staff she set,
To show that one heart was loyal yet.
Up the street came the rebel tread,
Stonewall Jackson riding ahead.

Under his slouched hat, left and right,
He glanced; the old flag met his sight.
'Halt!' – the dust-brown ranks stood fast.
'Fire!' – out blazed the rifle blast.

It shivered the window, pane and sash;
It rent the banner with seam and gash.
Quick, as it fell, from the broken staff
Dame Barbara snatched the silken scarf;

She leaned far out on the window sill,
And shook it forth with a royal will.
'Shoot, if you must, this old grey head,
But spare your country's flag,' she said.

A shade of sadness, a blush of shame,
Over the face of the leader came;
The noble nature within him stirred
To life, at that woman's deed and word.

Who touches a hair on yon grey head
Dies like a dog! March on!' he said.
All day long through Frederick Street
Sounded the tread of marching feet;
All day long the free flag toss'd
Over the heads of the rebel host;
Ever its torn folds rose and fell
On the loyal winds that loved it well.

And through the hill-gaps sunset light
Shone over it with a warm good-night,
Barbara Frietchie's work is o'er,
And the rebel rides on his raids no more.

*John Greenleaf Whittier*

# The oxen

Christmas Eve, and twelve of the clock.
    'Now they are all on their knees,'
An elder said as we sat in a flock
    By the embers in hearthside ease.

We pictured the meek mild creatures where
    They dwelt in their strawy pen,
Nor did it occur to one of us there
    To doubt they were kneeling then.

So fair a fancy few would weave
    In these years! Yet, I feel,
If someone said on Christmas Eve,
    'Come; see the oxen kneel

'In the lonely barton[1] by yonder coomb[2]
    Our childhood used to know,'
I should go with him in the gloom,
    Hoping it might be so.

*Thomas Hardy*

[1] farmyard
[2] valley

# The eve of Christmas

It was the evening before the night
That Jesus turned from dark to light.

Joseph was walking round and round,
And yet he moved not on the ground.

He looked into the heavens, and saw
The pole stood silent, star on star.

He looked into the forest: there
The leaves hung dead upon the air.

He looked into the sea, and found
It frozen, and the lively fishes bound.

And in the sky, the birds that sang
Not in feathered clouds did hang.

Said Joseph: 'What is this silence all?'
An angel spoke: 'It is no thrall.

But is a sign of great delight:
The Prince of Love is born this night.'

And Joseph said: 'Where may I find
This wonder?' – 'He is all mankind,

Look, he is both farthest, nearest,
Highest and lowest, of all men the dearest.'

Then Joseph moved, and found the stars
Moved with him, and the evergreen airs,

The birds went flying, and the main
Flowed with its fishes once again.

And everywhere they went, they cried:
'Love lives, when all had died!'

*In Excelsis Gloria!*

*James Kirkup*

# Joseph was an old man

Joseph was an old man,
    And an old man was he,
When he wedded Mary
    In the land of Galilee.

Joseph and Mary walked
    Through an orchard good,
Where was cherries and berries
    So red as any blood.

Joseph and Mary walked
    Through an orchard green,
Where was berries and cherries
    As thick as might be seen.

O then bespoke Mary,
       So meek and so mild,
'Pluck me one cherry, Joseph,
       For I am with child.'

O then bespoke Joseph
       With words so unkind,
'Let him pluck thee a cherry
       That brought thee with child.'

O then bespoke the babe
       Within his mother's womb,
'Bow down then the tallest tree
       For my mother to have some.'

Then bowed down the highest tree
       Unto his mother's hand:
Then she cried 'See, Joseph,
       I have cherries at command!'

O then bespake Joseph –
       'I have done Mary wrong;
But cheer up, my dearest,
       And be not cast down.

O eat your cherries, Mary,
       O eat your cherries now;
O eat your cherries, Mary,
       That grow upon the bough.'

Then Mary plucked a cherry
    As red as the blood;
Then Mary went home
    With her heavy load.

*Unknown medieval author*

# Ballad of the bread man

Mary stood in the kitchen
Baking a loaf of bread.
An angel flew in through the window.
We've a job for you, he said.

God in his big gold heaven,
Sitting in his big blue chair,
Wanted a mother for his little son.
Suddenly saw you there.

Mary shook and trembled,
It isn't true what you say.
Don't say that, said the angel.
The baby's on its way.

Joseph was in the workshop
Planing a piece of wood.
The old man's past it, the neighbours said,
That girl's been up to no good.

And who was that elegant feller,
They said, in the shiny gear?
The things they said about Gabriel
Were hardly fit to hear.

Mary never answered,
Mary never replied.
She kept the information,
Like the baby, safe inside.

It was election winter.
They went to vote in town.
When Mary found her time had come
The hotels let her down.

The baby was born in an annex
Next to the local pub.
At midnight, a delegation
Turned up from the Farmer's Club.

They talked about an explosion
That cracked a hole in the sky,
Said they'd been sent to the Lamb & Flag
To see god come down from on high.

A few days later a bishop
And a five-star general were seen
With the head of an African country
In a bullet-proof limousine.

We've come, they said, with tokens
For the little boy to choose.
Told the tale about war and peace
In the television news.

After them came the soldiers
With rifle and bomb and gun,
Looking for enemies of the state.
The family had packed and gone.

When they got back to the village
The neighbours said to a man,
That boy will never be one of us,
Though he does what he blessed well can.

He went round to all the people
A paper crown on his head.
Here is some bread from my father.
Take, eat, he said.

Nobody seemed very hungry,
Nobody seemed to care.
Nobody saw the god in himself
Quietly standing there.

He finished up in the papers.
He came to a very bad end.
He was charged with bringing the living to life.
No man was that prisoner's friend.

There's only one kind of punishment
To fit that kind of a crime.
They rigged a trial and shot him dead.
They were only just in time.

They lifted the young man by the leg,
They lifted him by the arm,
They locked him in a cathedral
In case he came to harm.

They stored him safe as water
Under seven rocks.
One Sunday morning he burst out
Like a jack-in-the-box.

Through the town he went walking.
He showed them the holes in his head.
How do you want any loaves? he cried.
Not today, they said.

*Charles Causley*

# Innocent's song

Who's that knocking on the window,
Who's that standing at the door,
What are all those presents
Lying on the kitchen floor?

Who is the smiling stranger
With hair as white as gin,
What is he doing with the children
And who could have let him in?

Why has he rubies on his fingers,
A cold, cold crown on his head,
Why, when he caws his carol,
Does the salty snow run red?

Why does he ferry my fireside
As a spider on a thread,
His fingers made of fuses
And his tongue of gingerbread?

Why does the world before him
Melt in a million suns,
Why do his yellow, yearning eyes
Burn like saffron buns?

Watch where he comes walking
Out of the Christmas flame,
Dancing, double-talking:

Herod is his name.

*Charles Causley*

# Every dog his day

When all the world is young, lad,
    And all the trees are green;
And every goose a swan, lad,
    And every lass a queen;
Then hey for boot and horse, lad,
    And round the world away;
Young blood must have its course, lad,
    And every dog his day.

When all the world is old, lad,
    And all the trees are brown;
And all the sport is stale, lad,
    And all the wheels run down;
Creep home, and take your place there,
    The spent and maimed among:
God grant you find one face there,
    You loved when all was young.

*Charles Kingsley*

# Won't you marry me?

'Soldier, soldier, won't you marry me?'
    *It's O the fife and drum!*
'How can I marry such a pretty girl as you
    When I've got no hat to put on!'

Off to the tailor's she did go
    As fast as she could run,
Brought him back the finest that was there:
    Now, soldier, put it on!

'Soldier, soldier, won't you marry me?'
    *It's O the fife and drum!*
'How can I marry such a pretty girl as you
    When I've got no coat to put on!'

Back to the tailor's she did go
    As fast as she could run,
Brought him back the finest that was there:
    Now, soldier, put it on!

'Soldier, soldier, won't you marry me?'
    *It's O the fife and drum!*
'How can I marry such a pretty girl as you
    When I've got no shoes to put on!'

Off to the shoe-shop she did go
    As fast as she could run,
Brought him back the finest that were there:
    Now, soldier, put them on!

'Soldier, soldier, won't you marry me?'
    *It's O the fife and drum!*
'How can I marry such a pretty girl as you
    When I've a wife and babies at home!'

*Not known*

# My Lady Greensleeves

Alas! my love, ye do me wrong
  To cast me off discourteously;
And I have lovèd you so long,
  Delighting in your company.
    *Greensleeves was all my joy,*
    *Greensleeves was my delight;*
    *Greensleeves was my heart of gold,*
      *And who but Lady Greensleeves.*

I bought the petticoats of the best,
  The cloth so fine as fine as might be:
I gave thee jewels for thy chest,
  And all this cost I spent on thee,
    *Greensleeves was all my joy,*
    *Greensleeves was my delight;*
    *Greensleeves was my heart of gold,*
      *And who but Lady Greensleeves.*

Thy smock of silk, both fair and white,
  With gold embroidered gorgeously:
Thy petticoat of sendal[1] right:
  And these I bought thee gladly.
    *Greensleeves was all my joy,*
    *Greensleeves was my delight;*
    *Greensleeves was my heart of gold,*
      *And who but Lady Greensleeves.*

fine linen

Greensleeves now farewell! adieu!
   God I pray to prosper thee:
For I am still thy lover true–
    Come once again and love me.
      *Greensleeves was all my joy,*
      *Greensleeves was all my delight;*
      *Greensleeves was my heart of gold,*
      *And who but Lady Greensleeves.*

*Not known*

# Midsummer night lullaby

You spotted snakes with double tongue,
   Thorny hedgehogs, be not seen;
Newts and blind-worms, do no wrong;
   Come not near our fairy queen.

   *Philomel, with melody,*
   *Sing in our sweet lullaby;*
   *Lulla, lulla, lullaby; lulla, lulla, lullaby:*
   *Never harm,*
   *Nor spell, nor charm,*
   *Come our lovely lady nigh;*
   *So, good night, with lullaby.*

Weaving spiders, come not here;
   Hence, you long-legg'd spinners, hence!
Beetles black, approach not near;
   Worm nor snail, do no offence.

*Philomel, with melody,*
*Sing in our sweet lullaby;*
*Lulla, lulla, lullaby; lulla, lulla, lullaby:*
*Never harm,*
*Nor spell nor charm,*
*Come our lovely lady nigh;*
*So, good night, with lullaby.*

William Shakespeare

# Puck's song

See you the dimpled track that runs,
    All hollow through the wheat?
O that was where they hauled the guns
    That smote King Philip's fleet.

See you our little mill that clacks,
    So busy by the brook?
She has ground her corn and paid her tax
    Ever since Domesday Book.

See you our stilly woods of oak,
    And the dread ditch beside?
O that was where the Saxons broke,
    On the day that Harold died.

See you the windy levels spread
    About the gates of Rye?
O that was where the Northmen fled,
    When Alfred's ships came by.

See you our pastures wide and lone,
    Where the red oxen browse?
O there was a City thronged and known,
    Ere London boasted a house.

And see you, after rain, the trace
    Of mound and ditch and wall?
O that was a Legion's camping-place,
    When Cæsar sailed from Gaul.

And see you marks that show and fade,
    Like shadows on the Downs?
O they are the lines the Flint Men made,
    To guard their wondrous towns.

Trackway and Camp and City lost,
    Salt Marsh where now is corn –
Old Wars, old Peace, old Arts that cease,
    And so was England born!

She is not any common Earth,
    Water or wood or air,
But Merlin's Isle of Gramarye,
    Where you and I will fare!

*Rudyard Kipling*

# The dwarf

'Now, Jinnie, my dear, to the dwarf be off,
    That lives in Barberry Wood,
And fetch me some honey, but be sure you don't laugh, –
    He hates little girls that are rude, are rude,
      He hates little girls that are rude.'

Jane tapped at the door of the house in the wood,
    And the dwarf looked over the wall,
He eyed her so queer, 'twas as much as she could
    To keep from laughing at all, at all,
      To keep from laughing at all.

His shoes down the passage came clod, clod, clod,
    And when he opened the door,
Ho croaked so harsh, 'twas as much as she could
    To keep from laughing the more, the more,
      To keep from laughing the more.

As there, with his bushy red beard, he stood,
    Pricked out to double its size,
He squinted so cross, 'twas as much as she could
    To keep the tears out of her eyes, her eyes,
      To keep the tears out of her eyes.

He slammed the door, and went clod, clod clod,
    But while in the porch she bides,
He squealed so fierce, 'twas as much as she could
    To keep from cracking her sides, her sides,
      To keep from cracking her sides.

He threw a pumpkin over the wall,
    And melons and apples beside,
So thick in the air that to see 'em all fall,
      She laughed and laughed, till she cried, cried, cried,
        Jane laughed and laughed till she cried.

Down fell her teardrops a pit-apat-pat,
    And red as a rose she grew; -
'Kah! Kah!' said the dwarf, 'is it crying you're at?
      It's the very worst thing you could do, do, do,
        It's the very worst thing you could do.'

He slipped like a monkey up into a tree,
    He shook her down cherries like rain;
'See how,' says he, cheeping, 'a blackbird I be,
      Laugh, laugh, little Jinnie, again-gain-gain,
        Laugh, laugh, little Jinnie, again!'

Ah me! what a strange, what a gladsome duet
    From a house in the deeps of a wood!
Such shrill and such harsh voices never met yet
      A-laughing as loud as they could, could, could,
        A-laughing as loud as they could.

Come Jinnie, come dwarf, cocksparrow, and bee,
    There's a ring gaudy-green in the dell,
Sing, sing, ye sweet cherubs, that flit in the tree;
      La! who can draw tears from a well, well, well,
        Who ever drew tears from a well!

*Walter de la Mare*

# John Barleycorn

There was three kings into the East,
 Three kings both great and high,
And they hae sworn a solemn oath,
 John Barleycorn should die.

They took a plough and ploughed him down,
 Put clods upon his head,
And they hae sworn a solemn oath,
 John Barleycorn was dead.

But the cheerful spring came kindly on,
 And showers began to fall;
John Barleycorn got up again,
 And sore surprised them all.

The sultry suns of summer came,
 And he grew thick and strong,
His head well armed wi' pointed spears,
 That no one should him wrong.

The sober autumn entered mild,
 When he grew wan and pale;
His bending joints and drooping head
 Showed he began to fail.

His colour sickened more and more,
 He faded into age;
And then his enemies began
 To show their deadly rage.

They've ta'en a weapon long and sharp,
 And cut him by the knee;
And tied him fast upon the cart,
 Like a rogue for forgerie.

They laid him down upon his back,
 And cudgelled him full sore;
They hung him up before the storm,
 And turned him o'er and o'er.

They fillèd up a darksome pit
 With water to the brim,
They heavèd in John Barleycorn,
 There let him sink or swim.

They laid him out upon the floor,
 To work him further woe,
And still, as signs of life appeared,
 They tossed him to and fro.

They wasted, o'er a scorching flame,
 The marrow of his bones;
But a miller used him worst of all,
 For he crushed him 'tween two stones.

And they hae ta'en his very heart's blood,
 And drank it round and round;
And still the more and more they drank,
 Their joy did more abound.

John Barleycorn was a hero bold,
    Of noble enterprise;
For if you do but taste his blood,
    'Twill make your courage rise.

Then let us toast John Barleycorn,
    Each man a glass in hand;
And may his great posterity
    Ne'er fail in old Scotland!

*Not known*

# The two witches

O, sixteen hundred and ninety one,
Never was year so well begun,
Backsy-forsy[1] and inside-out,
The best of all years to ballad about.

On the first fine day of January
I ran to my sweetheart Margery
And tossed her over the roof so far
That down she fell like a shooting star.

But when we two had frolicked and kissed
She clapped her fingers about my wrist
And tossed me over the chimney stack,
And danced on me till my bones did crack.

1691 reads the same back-to-front

Then, when she had laboured to ease my pain,
We sat by the stile of Robin's Lane,
She in a hare and I in a toad
And puffed at the clouds till merry they glowed.

We spelled our loves until close of day.
I wished her good-night and walked away,
But she put out a tongue that was long and red
And swallowed me down like a crumb of bread.

*Robert Graves*

# The little creature

Twinkum, twankum, twirlum and twitch –
My great grandam – She was a Witch.
Mouse in wainscot, Saint in niche –
My great grandam – She was a Witch;
Deadly nightshade flowers in a ditch –
My great grandam – She was a Witch;
Long though the shroud, it grows stitch by stitch –
My great grandam – She was a Witch;
Wean your weakling before you breech –
My great grandam – She was a Witch;
The fattest pig's but a double flitch –
My great grandam – She was a Witch;
Nightjars rattle, owls scritch –
My great grandam – She was a Witch.

Pretty and small,
A mere nothing at all,
Pinned up sharp in the ghost of a shawl,
She'd straddle her down to the kirkyard wall
And mutter and whisper and call,
And call . . .

Red blood out and black blood in,
My Nannie says I'm a child of sin.
How did I choose me my witchcraft kin?
Know I as soon as dark's dreams begin
Snared is my heart in a nightmare's gin;
Never from terror I out may win;
So dawn and dusk I pine, peak, thin,
Scarcely knowing t'other from which –
My great grandam – She was a Witch.

*Walter de la Mare*

# A lyke-wake dirge

This ae[1] nighte, this ae nighte,
   *– Every nighte and alle,*
Fire and fleet and candle-lighte,
   *And Christe receive thy saule.*

When thou from hence away art past,
   *– Every nighte and alle,*
To Whinny-muir[2] thou com'st at last:
   *And Christe receive thy saule.*

If ever thou gavest hosen and shoon[3],
   *– Every nighte and alle,*
Sit thee down and put them on:
   *And Christe receive thy saule.*

If hosen and shoon thou ne'er gav'st nane
   *– Every nighte and alle,*
The whinnes sall prick thee to the bare bane;
   *And Christe receive thy saule.*

From Whinny-muir when thou may'st pass,
   *– Every nighte and alle,*
To Brig o' Dread thou com'st at last;
   *And Christe receive thy saule.*

[1] very night
[2] a moor covered with thistles (whinnies)
[3] socks and shoes

From Brig o' Dread when thou may'st pass,
  *– Every nighte and alle,*
To Purgatory fire thou com'st at last;
  *And Christe receive thy saule.*

If ever thou gavest meat or drink,
  *– Every nighte and alle,*
The fire sall never make thee shrink;
  *And Christe receive thy saule.*

If meat or drink thou ne'er gav'st nane,
  *– Every nighte and alle,*
The fire will burn thee to the bare bane;
  *And Christe receive thy saule.*

This ae nighte, this ae nighte,
  *– Every nighte and alle,*
Fire and fleet and candle-lighte,
  *And Christe receive thy saule.*

*Not known*

# Micky Thumps

As I was going down Treak Street
For half a pound of treacle,
Who should I meet but my old friend Micky Thumps?
He said to me, 'Wilt thou come to our wake?'
 I thought a bit,
 I thought a bit,
 I said I didn't mind:
 So I went.

As I was sitting on our doorstep
Who should come by but my old friend Micky Thumps' brother?
He said to me, 'Wilt thou come to our house?
Micky is ill.'
 I thought a bit,
 I thought a bit,
 I said I didn't mind:
 So I went.

And he were ill.
He were gradely ill.
He said to me,
'Wilt thou come to my funeral, mon, if I die?'
 I thought a bit,
 I thought a bit,
 I said I didn't mind:
 So I went.

And it were a funeral.
Some stamped on his grave:
Some spat on his grave:
But I scraped my eyes out for my old friend Micky Thumps.

*Not known*

# Neighbours

Old Mrs Thompson down the road is dead.
The maid knew first from what the milkman said;
He heard on Sunday she was very bad,
And as they dust, they are sorry, stirred and glad.

One day soon I shall die,
As still as Mrs Thompson I shall lie;
And in her house that April day
The maids of the new family will say
That Mrs Jones, who was me, has passed away.
They will know first, because the fish-boy heard;
And as they dust, be sorry, glad, and stirred.

*Frances Cornford*

# All but blind

All but blind
    In his chambered hole
Gropes for worms
    The four-clawed Mole.

All but blind
    In the evening sky
The hooded Bat
    Twirls softly by.

All but blind
    In the burning day
The Barn-Owl blunders
    On her way.

And blind as are
    These three to me,
So, blind to Some-One
    I must be.

*Walter de la Mare*

# A hymn

Our God, our help in ages past,[1]
    Our hope for years to come,
Our shelter from the stormy blast,
    And our eternal home.

Beneath the shadow of thy throne
    Thy Saints have dwelt secure;
Sufficient is thine arm alone,
    And our defence is sure.

Before the hills in order stood,
    Or Earth received her frame,
From everlasting thou art God,
    To endless years the same.

A thousand ages in thy sight
    Are like an evening gone;
Short as the watch that ends the night
    Before the rising sun.

Time, like an ever-rolling stream,
    Bears all its sons away;
They fly forgotten as a dream
    Dies at the opening day.

*Isaac Watts*

[1] this is the original first line. Charles Wesley, another great writer of hymns, changed it to *O God, our help in ages past.*

# Psalm 121

I will lift up mine eyes unto the hills,
From whence cometh my help.
My help cometh from the Lord,
Which made heaven and earth.

He will not suffer thy foot to be moved:
He that keepeth thee will not slumber.
Behold, he that keepeth Israel
Shall neither slumber nor sleep.

The Lord is thy keeper:
The Lord is thy shade upon thy right hand.
The sun shall not smite thee by day,
Nor the moon by night.

The Lord shall preserve thee from all evil:
He shall preserve thy soul.
The Lord shall preserve thy going out and thy coming in
From this time forth, and even for evermore.

*From the Authorised Version of The Bible*

# Psalm 100

Make a joyful noise unto the Lord, all ye lands.
Serve the Lord with gladness;
Come before his presence with singing.
Know ye that the Lord he is God:
It is he that made us, and not we ourselves;
We are his people, and the sheep of his pasture.
Enter into his gates with thanksgiving,
And into his courts with praise:
Be thankful unto him, and bless his name.
For the Lord is good; his mercy is everlasting;
And his truth endureth to all generations.

*From the Authorised Version of the Bible*

# God be in my head

God be in my head,
    And in my understanding;

God be in mine eyes,
    And in my looking;

God be in my mouth,
    And in my speaking;

God be in my heart,
    And in my thinking;

God be at mine end,
    And at my departing.

*Fifteenth-century hymn*

# Eternity

He who bends to himself a joy
Does the winged life destroy;
But he who kisses the joy as it flies
Lives in eternity's sun rise.

*William Blake*

# Index of first lines